CALL TO THE
RESCUE

CALL TO THE
RESCUE

THE STORY OF THE MARINE MAMMAL CENTER

BY JOE QUIRK

FOREWORD BY PHILIPPE COUSTEAU

CHRONICLE BOOKS
SAN FRANCISCO

The Marine
Mammal Center™

This edition published exclusively for The Marine Mammal Center by Chronicle Books LLC.

Text copyright © 2009 by Joe Quirk.
Foreword copyright © 2009 by Philippe Cousteau.
Photographs copyright © 2009 by The Marine Mammal Center except for the following: pages 10, 23, 30, 47, 56, 57, 76, 86, and 89 (top image) copyright © 2009 by Stan Keiser; pages 72, 83, 84, 87, and 92 copyright © 2009 by NOAA.

The Marine Mammal Center gratefully acknowledges the following individuals and organizations for use of their photographs: Algalita Marine Research Foundation, Marie DeStefanis, Deborah Gabris, GOGA, Melanie Heck, Stan Jensen, Stan Keiser, Linda J. Lowenstine/The University of California, Pat Morris, NMFS NOAA Permit # 932-1489-09, Ingrid Overgard, Ken Padilla, Sue Pemberton, Gina Sanfillipo, Chris Shields, Misuzu Toyama, and Chris Whittier.

ISBN 978-0-8118-7007-8

Library of Congress Cataloging-in-Publication Data available under ISBN 978-0-8118-7008-5

Manufactured in the United States of America.

Design by Lori Barra, TonBo Designs.
Design and color production by Peter Truskier,
    Premedia Systems, Inc.
Design Assistant: Bry Mulrennan
This book has been set in Dante, Fournier, and Gotham.

Datsun is a registered trademark of Nissan Jidosha Kabushiki Kaisha Company; Duke Energy is a registered trademark of Duke Energy Corporation; Dumpster is a registered trademark of Dempster Brothers, Inc.; Exxon is a registered trademark of Exxon Mobil Corporation; Honda is a registered trademark of Honda Motor Co., Ltd; The Marine Mammal Center is a registered trademark of The Marine Mammal Center; Porta Potti is a registered trademark of Thetford Corporation; Rubbermaid is a registered trademark of Rubbermaid, Inc.; Six Flags and Marine World amusement parks are registered trademarks of Six Flags Theme Parks, Inc.

10 9 8 7 6 5 4 3 2 1

Chronicle Books LLC
680 Second Street
San Francisco, California 94107
www.chroniclebooks.com/custom

PAGE 2: The graceful California sea lion has roamed the coasts for millions of years. **PAGE 3:** Gregarious California sea lions assemble on beaches in groups of a thousand or more. **PAGE 5:** Curiosity is a defining characteristic of the California sea lion.

This book is dedicated to all past and present volunteers, staff, and board members of The Marine Mammal Center and to the memory of three of our most generous benefactors: Geoffrey C. Hughes, William Kimball, and Carol Ann Read.

The Marine Mammal Center gratefully acknowledges Merrill L. Magowan and Mark Magowan for their vision and guidance in the creation of this book.

contents

OPPOSITE: The magnificent northern elephant seal dives to depths of nearly a mile and travels up to 12,500 miles a year. Its biannual migration—to fast, shed fur, and battle for mates—is one of nature's most dramatic events.

foreword

by Philippe Cousteau

THE OCEANS ARE OUR GREATEST WILDERNESS, covering 70 percent of the earth, and supporting all life on this planet. The mammalian citizens of this kingdom are our greatest allies in understanding this vital environment. Like canaries in a coal mine, they are the first to suffer the devastating effects of contaminated seafood, deadly climate shifts, and increased competition for natural resources. These dynamics threaten the health of the oceans and thus all life on what my grandfather Jacques Cousteau called "our water planet."

Operating twenty-four hours a day, 365 days a year, the Marine Mammal Center is one of the largest rehabilitation and rescue organizations in the world, served by a world-renowned veterinary staff and a dedicated corps of more than eight hundred volunteers. I hope their tireless dedication to service inspires you to join our common cause to save marine mammals.

"If man in a time of need seeks deeper knowledge concerning himself, then he must explore those animal horizons from which we have made our quick little march."

—*Robert Ardrey*, African Genesis, *1961*

introduction

LESS THAN 5 MILES FROM SAN FRANCISCO, nestled in the Marin Headlands above a lagoon and quiet beach frequented by surfers and seabirds, is a small marine mammal hospital. The idyllic setting belies the important research that the Marine Mammal Center is doing in the name of science and the environment. It's more than just a research hospital, though;

PAGE 10-11: Pacific harbor seal pups are nursed mostly on land for about four weeks, during which time they will gain 1 to 1.5 pounds per day. They may double in weight from the time they are born to the time that they are weaned.

ABOVE: Students in the Center's Marine Science Discovery Program collect data aboard *The Adventure Cat*.

OPPOSITE: This group of elephant seals is gathered to molt their fur at Año Nuevo State Natural Reserve, the site of the largest mainland breeding colony in the world for the northern elephant seal.

it is also a place that rings with the laughter of schoolchildren on field trips, the calls of seal pups in pens, and the lively discussions of volunteers and staff as they respond to rescue calls and rehabilitate animals.

The Marine Mammal Center was founded in 1975 by a man who loved wild animals. The clinic started out with little more than three volunteers, a bathtub, and some chicken-wire fencing—and in the beginning, most of the patients died.

Now, more than thirty years later, with state-of-the-art facilities, the Center is a world leader in marine mammal medicine, scientific research, education, and environmental stewardship. Within the Center's 600-mile rescue range, between five hundred and one thousand stranded marine mammals are rescued every year, and nearly half of these patients are rehabilitated and returned to the ocean. Marine biologists from every corner of the globe benefit from research conducted at the Center, which has an open-door policy of freely sharing its findings. Tens of thousands of schoolchildren attend its education programs each year, some of them coming back as adults to volunteer. And the diseases that its scientists have discovered in animals have alerted us to dangers that humans might soon face, demonstrating an intimate link between the health of marine mammals and the health of people. Seals and sea lions swim near urban coasts, eat the same fish that we do, and suffer from diseases that could afflict humans, which is why scientists at the Marine Mammal Center call them "the sentinels of the sea."

chapter 1

IN 1964 LLOYD SMALLEY BECAME CURATOR at the Junior Museum of Marin in San Rafael, California. Today it's called WildCare and is a wildlife rehabilitation center. In the early years, it was dedicated to educating children about their local natural world. It consisted of dioramas depicting local habitats and live animal exhibits, including fence lizards, hawks, eagles, a large bear, two mountain lions, and one harbor seal. In 1965 Smalley was presented with a dilemma. Solving the problem soon became his personal mission.

At the time, stranded seals and sea lions were visibly suffering alone on Bay Area beaches. Many beachgoers couldn't bring themselves to walk past these unfortunate creatures, especially the newborn harbor seal pups, which, amid their many heartrending vocalizations, have an uncanny knack

"The greatness of a nation can be judged by the way its animals are treated."

—*Mahatma Gandhi*

PAGE 15: Northern elephant seals travel thousands of miles to breed on beaches, where they fast for months and lose about a third of their body weight.

ABOVE: Lloyd Smalley, the Center's founder, with an early patient.

for saying "Maa." So well-meaning people would load these sick and potentially dangerous pinnipeds (mammals with flippers) into their cars and deliver them to the museum in the hopes that the animals would receive treatment.

Smalley had to explain to the would-be rescuers that he worked for a science museum, not a marine mammal hospital. In fact, such a facility didn't even exist. Since the Humane Society didn't take in wild animals at that time, Smalley had to break the news—again and again—that there was just no place to take a sickly seal or a suffering sea lion. "So what are we supposed to do?" the rescuers would invariably ask.

By the end of 1965, Smalley agreed to take the ailing animals into the museum, and word quickly spread. Unfortunately, the majority of Smalley's first patients died. Little was known outside of the research community about marine mammal medicine and how to successfully treat the unique physiology that allows marine mammals to dive to 1,500 feet, hold their breath for more than an hour, lower their heart rate to six beats per minute, use their whiskers as hydrodynamic receptors to detect the movements of prey in the water, and migrate thousands of miles to feed and mate. After six years of struggle and experimentation, in May 1971, Smalley returned a rescued California sea lion that he'd named Cowboy

and a harbor seal that he'd named Bobby to the Bolinas Lagoon. Watching them swim out to sea, Smalley realized the cycle of rescue, rehabilitation, and release was not only possible, it could be perfected.

"The idea of a facility gradually began to take hold of my thoughts," recalls Smalley. "Imagine having the resources to perform efficient and timely rescues of injured, orphaned, or diseased marine mammals with a staff to develop expertise in handling and caring for such animals. Imagine an organization devoted to the scientific study of marine mammals that also provides education for the general public.

"There came a time when I realized that I needed to make a choice: Remain at the museum and continue with the rescue work as incidental to my other duties, or leave the museum and start up a project dedicated solely to marine mammals," says Smalley.

In 1972 Smalley received news that would bring his dream for a healthier future for marine mammals a little closer to reality. The U.S. Congress passed the Marine Mammal Protection Act, which cited the following findings:

> Some marine mammal species or stocks may be in danger of extinction or depletion as a result of human activities . . .
> There is inadequate knowledge of the ecology and population dynamics . . .

Marine mammals have proven to be resources of great international significance.

Although the Marine Mammal Protection Act revealed some harsh truths about the state of marine mammals, its findings and policies provided a catalyst for Smalley's career shift. With encouragement from his wife, Gayle, Smalley quit his job at the museum in the spring of 1973 and, by November, authored a proposal to establish the California Marine Mammal Center. He submitted it to the county supervisor for an endorsement, as well as to several local business leaders who had long supported Smalley's projects at the museum and knew of his passion.

Paul Maxwell, a zoologist at the San Francisco Zoo, had been director of the Junior Museum of Marin when Smalley was curator. He found Smalley's proposal irresistible and joined him in his efforts to establish the Center. Smalley then contacted a friend who was knowledgeable in local politics, Pat Arrigoni, for help in getting additional endorsements and information on potential sites, including the use of government property. Her husband, Peter, was a member of the Marin County Board of Supervisors. He made the government connections, without which the permits never would have been approved.

THE VOICE OF EVIL?

When Peter Jackson, director of *The Lord of the Rings*, asked the sound designer to find the most terrifying, alien voice in the world to portray his evil orcs, he used the voice of this little guy. The cackle of the fearsome orcs, rising from the furnace in the Hall of the Mountain King, is actually the sound of elephant seal pups crying out for milk. By recording baby elephant seal shrieks and raising them an octave, sound designers were also able to create the shrill sound of the Nazgûl (the Nine), a.k.a. the Black Riders.

Animals at the Marine Mammal Center have been terrifying moviegoers for years. Remember *Jurassic Park*? Stephen Spielberg needed a voice for a mother triceratops. Who better to provide the voice of a 7-ton dinosaur than an elephant seal pup?

Sorry, our movie star seals won't sign autographs.

ABOVE: This juvenile northern elephant seal rides in style as he is transported to a clean pen.

OPPOSITE: Marine mammals are so social that volunteers are trained to avoid eye contact to prevent the animals from bonding permanently with humans.

LEFT: Despite their charm, marine mammals are wild animals that must feed, breed, and avoid predators.

ABOVE: A rescue effort is not fully successful until the rehabilitated animal creates the next generation. **LEFT:** Northern elephant seals were slaughtered wholesale in the 1800s for the oil that could be rendered from their blubber. By 1892 only 50 to 100 individuals were left. After a century of protection laws, the population has grown to about 160,000.

ABOVE: The Center is built on the former site of a Nike missile base at Fort Cronkhite, where during the cold war, soldiers waited for an enemy that never came.
RIGHT: The original guard shack served as the Center's information hut for more than thirty years.

Though no money was pledged, political support was enough to send Lloyd and Gayle Smalley on a whirlwind of salesmanship, sweeping through bureaucracies with their vision of animal rescue and release and scientific research. The National Oceanic and Atmospheric Administration (NOAA) and the Marine Mammal Commission readily granted permits. Soon the pair submitted a grant proposal to the Marin County School District to establish an educational program at the Center.

The Center's cofounders—Pat Arrigoni, Paul Maxwell, and Lloyd Smalley—scouted for sites near seal and sea lion habitats. While eating lunch at a coffee shop on Sir

Francis Drake Boulevard, Maxwell threw out a zany idea: "Why don't we use the abandoned Nike missile base at Fort Cronkhite?"

Although the former base was designed to launch surface-to-air defense missiles, and despite the facts that no private citizen had ever been granted a permit to use government land (formerly belonging to the U.S. Army, the land was then owned by the National Park Service) and that competing plans to use the space had already been suggested, Smalley couldn't contain his enthusiasm.

"The buildings were a wreck; the windows had been knocked out," he recalls.

The Center's cofounders scouted for sites near seal and sea lion habitats. While eating lunch at a coffee shop on Sir Francis Drake Boulevard, Maxwell threw out a zany idea: "Why don't we use the abandoned Nike missile base at Fort Cronkhite?"

"They had been cannibalized by the army for parts. All of the circuit breakers were taken out, the light fixtures, plumbing fixtures . . ." But what really mattered was location, location, location.

The presentation the trio made to Bill Whalen, former superintendent of the Golden Gate National Recreation Area, earned them an unprecedented use permit, making the Center the first private citizen group in the country to be permitted use of national park property.

Smalley and a carpenter friend rolled up their sleeves. Walls went up; water and electric power were restored. The former "ready room," where army personnel waited for their duty shifts at the launch site, was remodeled into an emergency clinic, feed room, and all-purpose meeting room with a library. The guard shack became an office. The old guard-dog kennels were cleaned up and served as holding pens for seals and sea lions. Materials such as lumber, electric cable, window glass, and drywall were scrounged from local suppliers. Within a few months, the buildings, the underground missile silos, and the grounds had been converted into an animal hospital. To this day, staff call it "a whole new kind of coastal defense."

ABOVE: The fearsome antiballistic missiles are long gone, and today underground silos house the water filtration system.

"Organizing the Center was a process of **hard labor** and meetings at midnight. It survived for several years strictly on the sweat of **volunteers**; there were no salaries."

RIGHT: Nursing harbor seal mothers may leave their pups temporarily to forage at sea. Unfortunately, well-meaning passersby sometimes carry off the pups, thinking they are abandoned.

TOO FAST, TOO SMART

You may spot wild marine mammals suffering with rope entanglements, fishing lines, hooks, and packing straps that squeeze them like sausages; they may also have painful-looking scabs and lesions around their ensnarements. Scientists are often well aware of these animals and are aching to remove the hazardous objects. But the animals won't surrender to their human helpers until their health is so dire that they can barely move.

Natural selection ensures that marine mammals are hard to catch. Since sharks and orcas catch animals that are sick or weak, a marine mammal must tough it out at all costs. Rescuers might get within 50 feet of the animals, yet the animals always stay just out of reach.

TOP: Young pinnipeds like this Guadalupe fur seal who tear free from fishing nets are often slowly strangled by entanglements as they grow larger.
BOTTOM: A veterinarian uses extreme care to remove a fishing net.

NOAA's National Marine Fisheries Service issued a permit allowing the Center to rescue and rehabilitate a maximum of twenty-five pinnipeds per year in accordance with the Marine Mammal Protection Act. The California Marine Mammal Center (as it was called until 1991, when the Center decided to drop "California" from its name) was incorporated as a nonprofit in 1975, and the Smalleys hit the ground running. Lloyd worked twelve- to fifteen-hour days, six and sometimes seven days a week. On weekends, Gayle and his daughter worked with him.

Forty volunteers were trained with help from the California Academy of Sciences. After many failed attempts, a California sea lion named Herman was the first to be treated for infection from roundworms and tapeworms and successfully released into the ocean in May 1975. The same year, the Center launched the first scientific research project to acquire a fundamental understanding of the unique physiology of marine mammals in order to better treat them. By year's end, the Center had finally established itself as a successful scientific research center and animal hospital. The year 1976 was inaugurated when a two-week-old abandoned northern elephant seal pup, affectionately known as Francis, was picked up, rehabilitated, and released two weeks later.

Organizing the Center was a process of hard labor and meetings at midnight. It survived for several years strictly on the sweat of volunteers; there were no salaries.

In 1982 a grant from the San Francisco Foundation allowed the Center to hire its first full-time paid executive director, Peigin Barrett. Formalized education programs began, along with new departments: Animal Care, Training, Facilities, Volunteer, Animal Placement, and Education.

By 1983 the California Marine Mammal Center was growing faster than it could acquire funds. It had published four scientific papers, the first being "Nursing Care of Stranded Northern Elephant Seals," coauthored by Smalley, and it had more than two thousand contributing members. Yet the facilities were ramshackle: phone banks from a bankrupt company, washing machines from the flea market. In the early years, the official vehicle was Smalley's '74 Datsun pickup. "We looked like *Sanford and Son*," says Barrett.

A terrible El Niño year was followed by an even more terrible kidney disease outbreak in sea lions. More and more animals were arriving with mysterious ailments, straining the facility far beyond its original twenty-five-patient limit, requiring a change in the permit specifications.

In 1984 some 385 animals were admitted, and the Center was in the red. Barrett

HOW TO TELL A TRUE SEAL FROM AN EARED SEAL

Floppers vs. Walkers
Watch how they move on land:
- True seals flop across the ground on their bellies like giant slugs.
- Sea lions and fur seals walk on all four flippers, like bears.

Earflaps or Ear Holes?
Look at their ears:
- True seals have no earflaps, just ear holes.
- Sea lions and fur seals have small earflaps.

RIGHT: Don't let the cuteness fool you. Northern fur seal pups will bite anyone who dares to approach.

remembers crying because they owed $3,000 in fish bills and couldn't pay it.

Coincidentally, that same year, millionaire horse breeder Geoffrey C. Hughes visited the Center by chance. Hughes died soon after his visit, and after his death the Geoffrey C. Hughes Foundation was established. Its contributions to the Center have totaled more than $5.8 mil-

lion, making Hughes the ultimate angel investor. Thanks to the generosity of the Geoffrey C. Hughes Foundation and many other donors, the California Marine Mammal Center was no longer a mom-and-pop hospital that couldn't afford fish. It would soon amass the resources to become one of the most significant marine mammal hospitals and research centers in the world.

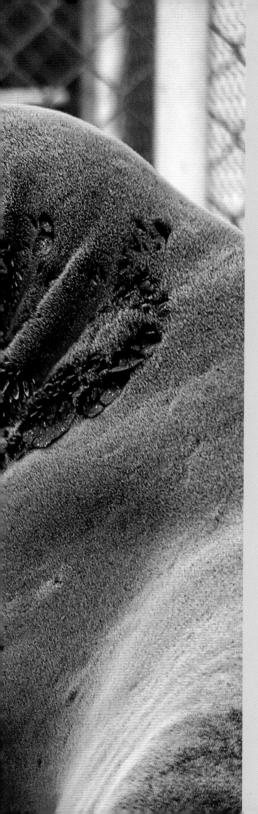

GEOFFREY C. HUGHES

The Marine Mammal Center has an odd tradition of captivating people who just happen to be hiking the Marin Headlands. One such person was millionaire horse breeder and opera lover Geoffrey C. Hughes.

Hughes was visiting from New York when he decided to take a hike. While following a trail high above Rodeo Beach, he heard an odd barking sound and went to investigate. Hughes stumbled upon a small group of people working at the modest Center and was smitten by one particular sea lion named Tuesday, who had been born at the Center. Hughes walked back down the hill, though he would soon return as more than an interested observer.

In 1988, after many long-distance phone calls to check in on Tuesday, he planned to visit her again. He called executive director Peigin Barrett from the San Francisco airport saying that he'd like to visit his "babies." Then he said that he didn't have his "driver."

All Barrett had was a Honda CRX hatchback with no backseat. So she drove it to San Francisco and found a strikingly handsome, somewhat frail, 6-foot-5 man with gray hair, dressed all in black, with a collared black cape—and Geoffrey C. Hughes. Hughes had neglected to tell Barrett that he was bringing a friend with him: the executive director of the San Francisco Opera. But the Honda only had two seats. Barrett turned to the distinguished opera director.

"Have you ever seen the Golden Gate Bridge while lying on your back?" she asked.

The three of them drove to the Center, the opera director reclining in the storage compartment of the hatchback, to see Tuesday the sea lion.

When Barrett recalls Mr. Hughes and his visit, she is effusive. "He didn't live on this planet. It was like he was a few feet off the ground. Geoffrey was walking joy. He was the embodiment of an individual who loved. And he loved the highest things. He loved the opera, and he loved these animals."

When Barrett said goodbye to Hughes, she gave him a big hug. "I'm going to tie a few things up," Hughes said mysteriously to her, "but I'm going to be seeing you."

Hughes died shortly thereafter, so he could not keep his promise to see his dear friend Peigin again. But one of the "few things" he "tied up" turned out to be a foundation that has been the Center's largest single benefactor, providing operational, endowment, and capital support.

LEFT: Two California sea lion patients. Juniper is marked for identification. Bellatrix 2 waits to have oil cleaned from her coat.

ABOVE AND RIGHT: Orphaned baby harbor seals admitted at the Center range from newborns with umbilical cords still attached to "weaners" with full sets of teeth.

FISHING FOR VOLUNTEERS

In 1976 Bob Wilson, an attorney who loved animals, heard a rumor that he could see a harbor seal up close. So he and his girlfriend hiked up into the Marin Headlands to find the elusive California Marine Mammal Center. Amid the ruins of the Nike missile base, they found some chicken wire, a few kiddie pools and bath tubs, a couple of seals, and Lloyd Smalley.

Among Smalley's many talents was his capacity to spot a sucker for animals. He asked Wilson to hold his flashlight for a second. Then he asked Wilson to give him a hand with the generator. Then he said, "Hey, could you help me carry this seal over there?"

Wilson had no idea what he was getting himself into. By the end of the day, Smalley offered Wilson the keys to the place.

"What for?" asked Wilson.

"Just in case," said Smalley.

"Just in case of what?"

The next day, Smalley gave Wilson a call. "I can't make it in today. Can you open up for me? The seals need somebody."

"From then on," laughs Wilson, recalling that day, "my girlfriend and I were the Saturday crew. It was a Tom Sawyer paint-the-fence sort of thing."

This would become a theme in Bob Wilson's relationship with the Center. During the next three decades, Wilson would serve in just about every capacity at the site, from cleaning pens to penning donor requests, from rescuing stranded animals to acting as board chairman. Meanwhile, Smalley would perfect his knack for twisting heartstrings. "My greatest talent is seeing the talent in other people," says Smalley.

LEFT: Scientists and volunteers perform an on-site necropsy (postmortem for animals) on a sperm whale for clues as to the cause of death. **ABOVE, TOP AND BOTTOM:** Volunteers quickly learn that animal rescue is not about cuddling, but dedication and discipline. The true reward of their work is not only helping animals, but also collecting data that can inform scientists about whole populations.

"It is amazing how much people get done if they do not worry about who gets the credit."

—*Swahili proverb*

chapter 2

WHEN LAURIE GAGE BECAME THE CENTER'S part-time veterinarian in 1980, she was also the veterinarian at the Six Flags Marine World theme park—and she was the *only* vet at both places, which meant that she was on call 24/7.

At night Laurie Gage and Peigin Barrett, along with some dedicated volunteers, would drive their cars up to the holding pens at the Center and administer tube feedings by headlights. Harbor seals and young sea lions were kept in airline containers. The harbor seal and elephant seal pups swam in plastic kiddie pools, and water filtration consisted of dumping the dirty water down the hill and then filling the pools with a hose. The power was often so erratic that they had to unplug the refrigerator in order to run the centrifuge. Late at night, they snuck seals into human hospitals for X-rays.

GNORT, THE TIGHTROPE WALKER

At the Marine Mammal Center, if a juvenile sea lion can't play without fighting, he gets put in a separate pen. But Gnort decided he had spent enough time in time-out.

"Oh no!" a few volunteers cried.

The volunteers were staring out the window to see Gnort balanced, *again*, on top of the 8-foot-high fence that separated the pens. Straddling the fence with all four flippers, he had shimmied his way across the top of two empty pens and dropped down into the third with his friends. But he hadn't played nicely, so volunteers had to capture the acrobat and bring him back to his original pen. Gnort had pretended to be docile until they left, then he quickly climbed the fence again and shimmied back across the top of the pens with renewed agility.

But overconfidence got the best of him when Gnort suddenly fell into an empty pen adjacent to his friends. The exhausted supervisor said, "Just leave him there."

Gnort settled for the compromise: He could still taunt his buddies through the chain-link fence.

PAGE 30: A juvenille California sea lion rests on offshore rocks.

RIGHT: Gnort posing proudly after a successful jailbreak.

Yet amid the fly-by-the-seat-of-your-pants atmosphere, the staff was incrementally establishing a scientific research institution. In the mid-1980s, the Center achieved a 100 percent survival rate among premature harbor seal pups.

Director of animal care Dawn Smith pushed a campaign to turn a crew of "bunny-huggers" into trained volunteers, and she helped set up the training program to safely clean sea otters after the devastating Exxon-Valdez oil spill in 1989.

While the executive director hustled around accumulating donations from hospitals that had upgraded to higher-tech instruments, veterinarian Laurie Gage wrote many of the protocols for taking blood, performing common veterinary procedures, and administering medicines, many of which are still in use today. Judi Gerber, the Center's first veterinary fellow, standardized the protocols for necropsy (a postmortem for animals) and applied a systematic study to the previous twenty years of data the Center had collected, which led to even more publications in peer-reviewed science journals. Gage's predecessor, Leslie Dierauf, invented a dozen medical procedures, a memorable one being a derivation of the Apgar score (a method for quickly assessing the health of newborn humans), which she adjusted for seal pups and named the "Pupgar

score." All the while, they kept precise records of every animal, slowly amassing a vast database for which the Center is now famous among marine biologists.

The slow accrual of innovations among these part-time vets and volunteers shifted the Center's reputation from being strictly a rehabilitation facility to a reputable veterinary hospital and research center. So long as the team got results and published their findings in respectable journals, nobody needed to know that they opened and closed the pens by twisting chicken wire around a post.

Veterinary fellow Kimberlee Beckmen's system of rapid diagnoses led to optimal recovery times and to the prompt alleviation of suffering for those patients with no chance of recovery. Postmortem diagnoses allowed Beckmen to discover that the silent killer of many elephant seal pups was a severe reaction to a parasite in a chamber of the heart. She developed a treatment regime and convinced a drug manufacturer to donate thousands of dollars worth of the necessary drug. "The Center enriched my life and advanced my career more than any other experience," Dr. Beckmen says.

As inspiring as it was, the harried, improvisational approach could only take the Center so far. There simply weren't sufficient resources to support the level of work needed. So in 1997 the board brought in Peggy Burks as executive director to restructure the Center into a more businesslike nonprofit model. For the next three years, the Center improved financial systems, formalized fundraising and communication functions, and strengthened the board, and a new Volunteer Council gave the volunteers an official voice. But Burks's most important contribution was her vision to rebuild the Center, setting the stage for a $30-million capital campaign.

It seemed like a huge, impossible challenge, but under Burks's leadership, the Geoffrey C. Hughes Harbor Seal Hospital and Surgery Center was completed, demonstrating a "yes we can" attitude that continued to prevail during subsequent years.

B. J. Griffin brought thirty-five years of experience with the National Park Service to the Marine Mammal Center when she signed on as executive director in 2000. During Griffin's tenure, $22 million was raised for the capital campaign. She led negotiations with patrons who donated land for the construction of the Center's field offices in Morro Bay (in San Luis Obispo County) and Moss Landing (in Monterey County). She was instrumental in expanding partnerships with the National Park Service, NOAA, and U.S. congressional delegations.

Staff veterinarian Dr. Marty Haulena turned the harbor seal hospital into a

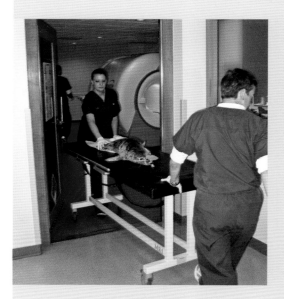

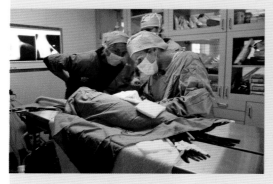

TOP: An injured harbor seal pup is wheeled out of the MRI after technicians scanned for ailments. **BOTTOM:** Veterinary surgeons work as a team to develop the medical innovations for which the Center is famous.

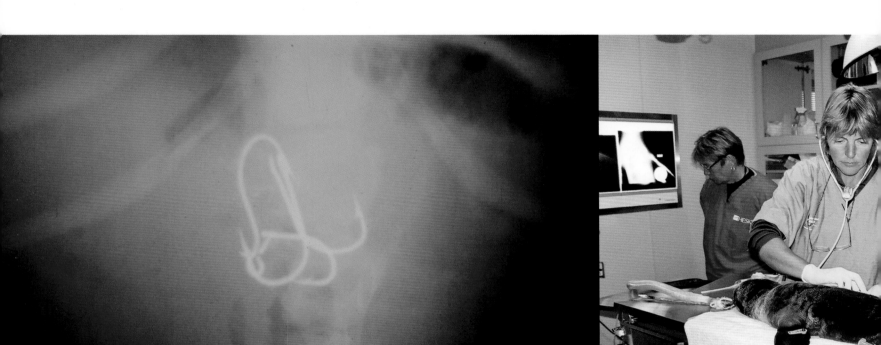

ABOVE: An X-ray reveals several fishhooks lodged in a sea lion's stomach. Many obstructions and all entanglements are man-made. **CENTER:** The Center established the safe benchmarks for marine mammal anesthesia that are utilized all over the world.

OPPOSITE, FAR RIGHT: Dr. Marty Haulena prepares a pacific harbor seal for surgery.

sophisticated surgical unit employing state-of-the-art diagnostic techniques such as electroencephalography (the measurement of electrical activity produced by the brain), endoscopy (minimally invasive surgery), and sonography (ultrasound). He developed surgical innovations for removing fishhooks and cataracts, spearheaded safe anesthetic protocols, and performed reconstructive surgery on the famous Scrappy, a Pacific harbor seal who was struck in the face and flipper by a boat propeller, requiring more than a dozen anesthetic procedures.

"We did surgeries in a rusty old military building where plaster and rust fell off walls and ceilings with some regularity," says Dr. Haulena. "A new surgical facility and hospital building were completed in 1999, and that changed everything. By the time I left the Marine Mammal Center in 2006, we had what I still think is the very best marine mammal hospital in terms of equipment and its capability to diagnose marine mammal disease."

Many veterinary students from around the world would study marine mammal

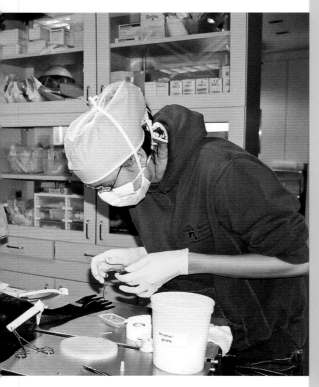

SEALS HAVE A SIXTH SENSE

Seeing, hearing, smelling, touching, tasting . . . and whiskering. Seals use their whiskers to detect tiny water movements. When a small fish swims, it leaves behind a tiny path of turbulence called a hydrodynamic trail. In the blind depths of the ocean, harbor seals can detect these vibrations using nothing but their ultrasensitive whiskers. And you thought whiskers were just to look dashing.

ABOVE: Seals often float upright like buoys, a swimming technique that's called bottling.

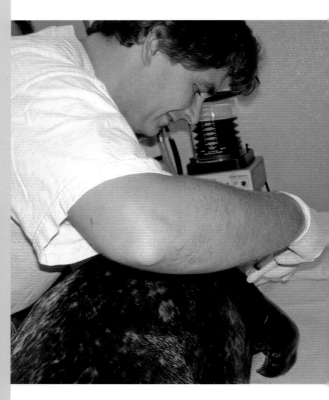

medicine under the direction of Haulena. Yet the humble doctor insists, "I'm pretty sure that I personally didn't make any great contribution to the organization. The Center was already made great by the efforts of those who had been there before." And Haulena isn't the only one to shrug off praise and instead give credit elsewhere.

"If you are ego-driven," says Dawn Smith, former director of animal care, "if it's important to you to be important, you're not going to survive. The Center is so much bigger than any individual."

In 1994, when Frances Gulland arrived to take the reins as full-time director of veterinary science, her predecessor, Laurie Gage, true to the low-budget atmosphere of the Center, placed a cardboard crown adorned with glued stars onto Dr. Gulland's head. With a grant from the Arthur and Elena Court Nature Watch Conservancy to support her work, Gulland entered an institution that was ready to take it to the next level.

"If you are ego-driven, if it's important to you to be important, you're not going to survive. The Center is so much bigger than any individual."

BELOW: This seal is wearing headphones to test his sensitivity to sound. The Center is working with the University of California at Santa Cruz to study how pinnipeds hear.

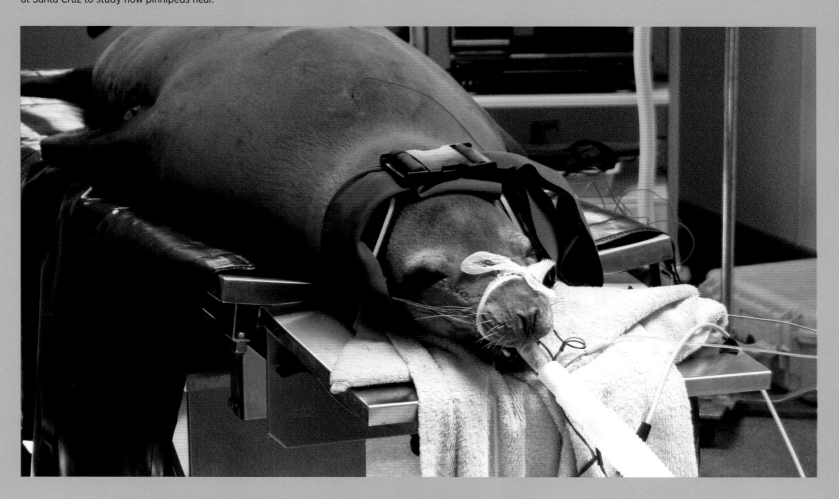

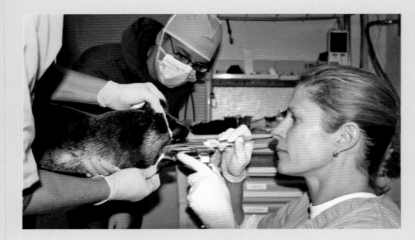

LEFT: Say *aaaah*! This northern fur seal pup is receiving state-of-the-art medical attention.
BELOW: A northern elephant seal pup has been dabbed with temporary grease paint so that volunteers won't confuse it with another pup.

ABOVE: The sagittal crest is a ridge on the skull that looks like a pompadour. It is a sign that this male California sea lion is fully mature.

FLASH GORDON

Seven female volunteers stand outside the animal pen in a football huddle, wearing the team uniform: plastic pants with suspenders, rubber boots, rubber gloves, and wooden shields at the ready. Inside the pen, a 500-pound male sea lion named Flash Gordon is perched at the top of the ramp that leads into his private pool, nose high in the air, chest out.

The leader of the huddle is calling the play in a whisper. "Okay, if he makes a break around the back, you two go around the other side and head him off. The rest of you block his right flank. I'm taking the left. No eye contact with the animals. Once we're in the pen, no talking allowed, so watch my eyes."

A new trainee, a petite woman, speaks in a squeak. "What should I do if he comes at me?"

"Whatever you're comfortable with," says the leader. The leader sports an impressive scar on both sides of her bicep from when a sea lion bit all the way through her arm.

The group leader glances at each face to make sure everybody is ready. Flash Gordon is crowned with a sagittal crest, which looks like a mohawk. The natural crown announces he has reached puberty, is at least five years old, and has something to prove.

She nods. The crew rushes into the sea lion enclosure like knights. With wooden shields and rubber body armor, they quickly assemble themselves into a human hallway designed to guide the sea lion off his perch and into a crate so that they can wheel him onto a scale and record how much his weight has changed since last week. Four blockers, two pushers, and a roving flank protector form a disciplined phalanx.

Spraying the ladies with a snort, the bull male deftly feints to the left, then lunges right and bites a chunk off the shield 6 inches

from the fingers of a volunteer, who takes it all in stride. The wooden shields read RESCUE, and most have bite marks.

Snorting like a freight train gathering speed, Flash Gordon charges down the ramp of his pool straight at the new volunteer, determined to break the human wall. The line is breached. The leader motions her head in a wordless command that says "Retreat!"

The seven women hustle out of the pen in formation, protecting their flanks. Flash Gordon ascends his perch and arches his chin to the sky, temporarily victorious.

ABOVE: An adult male California sea lion strikes a typical proud pose.

On October 10, 1985, a staff member at the Center spotted a humpback whale 50 yards offshore of Rodeo Beach. The next day the humpback surprised everyone when he swam under the Golden Gate Bridge and entered the San Francisco Bay. Residents, tourists, and the local press were delighted because humpback whales usually stay in very deep parts of the ocean. Marine mammal experts were worried for the same reason. Endangered humpback whales are social animals with a keen sense of direction, migrating south for the winter and north in the summer. Why would one head for inland waters?

The Center's research associates had been studying humpback whales for ten years, and they immediately tracked this particular stray in the coast guard's auxiliary boat and recorded his behavior. Meanwhile, the local press was having fun with the story. They named him "Humphrey the Wayward Whale." Humphrey was 45 feet long and weighed approximately 40 tons. For the next eleven days, the Center would respond to approximately one thousand phone calls a day about Humphrey. No one could have imagined that Humphrey was initiating a twenty-six-day ordeal.

As Humphrey headed for land, authorities declared him mentally ill and fretted about how to "clean up the carcass" when he would inevitably wash up on shore.

"Carcass?" said Peigin Barrett at the daylong meeting during which the fate of the mammal was discussed. "Let's concentrate on getting him out alive!"

But most people at the meeting didn't believe such a feat was possible. They thought he was too big, too heavy. Humphrey just wasn't worth the effort and expense.

The Center was determined to save Humphrey. But rescuers knew it would be a losing battle—unless a national spotlight was shone on the gentle giant. The Center had turned to the public for support many times, and the goodwill of empathetic citizens had never once let them down. Thus, the Center immediately began a public relations campaign and convinced then California state senator John Garamendi to take a stand on Humphrey's behalf.

The charming local story became national news when Humphrey swam up the Sacramento River. The freshwater made Humphrey's skin change color and peel, a sign that salt was being leeched from his system. Whales are more buoyant in saltwater, and Humphrey had to exert himself to stay afloat.

The Center had turned to the **public** for support many times, and the goodwill of empathetic citizens had **never** once let them down.

LEFT: Pacific harbor seals must spend about half their time on land when molting (shedding their fur). This onshore time is important to the life cycle and can be disturbed by human presence.

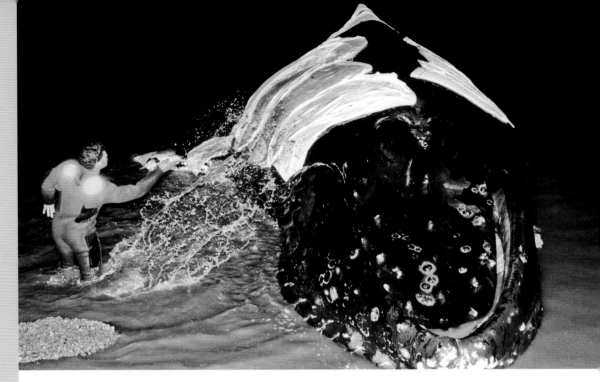

YOU FIND IT,
YOU NAME IT

Whoever reports or rescues the stranded animal gets to name it, and the names generally preserve the dignity of these noble animals: Goldilocks, Tuna Melt, Eggy Bagel. Some of the animals are named after charming stories of their behavior, like Sunnyside Up; others, like Uncle Dirty, are not so charming. In any case, allowing members of the public or rescue volunteers to name the animals not only personalizes their relationship with the animal that they help rescue, but the uniqueness generated by so many people guarantees a variety of names, so the Marine Mammal Center's vast database does not get confusing. The Center has rescued more than thirteen thousand animals, with few name repetitions, thanks to the creativity of an alert public.

Yet, Humphrey wouldn't stop swimming the wrong way up brackish estuaries. Eventually he traveled up a drainage canal that was only four times his own width, with cow pastures on either side. The water was full of pesticides recently flushed from nearby irrigation fields. He finally got himself stuck in a slough under a small bridge in the town of Rio Vista, 69 miles upriver. Authorities began using the word "carcass" again.

Within days of the story breaking, citizens offered their fishing boats and pleasure cruisers to help herd Humphrey out. Ultimately, thousands offered to volunteer, including an entrepreneur who allowed scientists to use his helicopter for surveillance. A scientist who discovered echolocation in dolphins proposed an ancient Japanese fishing technique known as *oikami*, whereby people in a flotilla of boats make a disagreeable racket by banging steel pipes. Meanwhile, the attractive sounds of humpback whales preparing to feed were broadcast underwater from a boat headed toward the open ocean. Conducted by another scientist, the underwater playback proved to be the first successful broadcast of its kind; after eight hours of whale sounds, Humphrey began his return trip to the sea. An escort of more than fifty boats and five hundred people herded Humphrey the Wayward Whale back toward the ocean. Humphrey spent a day swimming in the bay, slapping his pectoral fin, leaping out of the water, and generally cementing his fame before he swam under the Golden Gate Bridge out to the Pacific, twenty-six days after getting lost.

And then Barrett and the team of scientists witnessed something they swear they will never forget. After Humphrey passed under the Golden Gate Bridge to the cheers of onlookers, a long silence reigned. Suddenly, Humphrey *swam back*, surfaced near a boat, rolled over, looked up at everyone, dove, and disappeared. Among the marine mammal community, this is the all-time most inspiring "release story."

The showman would return for an encore five years later. In 1990 Humphrey the Wayward Whale was in trouble again, beached in a mudflat in the bay near Candlestick Park (renamed Monster Park in 2004). For three days, rescuers from the Marine Mammal Center and the U.S. Coast Guard were unable to free Humphrey, who was so mired in sticky mud that suction held him firm. Staff and volunteers kept his skin wet, and Dr. Laurie Gage monitored his respiration and took blood samples. Finally, a man from Redwood City volunteered his giant air compressor to pump air under Humphrey during high tide, which released him from the mud and enabled him to swim freely to deeper water. Humphrey has been sighted only once since then, at the Farallon Islands in 1991.

OPPOSITE AND RIGHT: Veterinarians and volunteers keep Humphrey's skin moist with wet towels and his eyes hydrated with saline.

ABOVE: Dawn, the baby humpback whale, breeches in the crowded San Francisco Bay. Ship strikes are a major cause of death and injury to whales. **LEFT:** The gray whale, like the one pictured, is a baleen whale, but unlike the humpback and blue whales, who take big gulps of water to feed on plankton, the gray whale feeds on amphipods by turning on its side and slurping mud from the ocean floor. All three use their baleen like a sieve to trap food. Gray whales are California's state marine mammal and are often observed in the Center's rescue range.

But this wasn't the end of wayward whales. In 2007 a mother humpback and her calf, affectionately dubbed Delta and Dawn, followed in Humphrey's fin strokes. They were first spotted on May 13, and both whales were suffering from infected cuts possibly caused by boat propellers. Despite efforts to get them to return to the sea, they continued their swim into brackish waters until they swam 90 miles upstream to Sacramento. John Garamendi became involved once again, this time as lieutenant governor, lending much-needed political clout for the new rescue effort. They were the first whales in the wild ever treated with antibiotics.

Eventually, the mother and daughter headed back toward the bay. After tarrying near the Rio Vista Bridge for ten days, they finally made it to the sea. Delta led young Dawn past the Golden Gate and into the Pacific on May 29.

In both of these highly publicized incidents, the Marine Mammal Center played a critical role in rescuing the whales and ensuring their safe return to the Pacific Ocean. And while successful rescue and rehabilitation is gratifying, as is the international attention brought to the cause, marine mammal experts are fighting a battle that is being escalated by increases in coastal populations of humans and shipping-channel traffic.

BLUE WHALE DEATHS INCREASING

Endangered blue whales, the largest animals ever to roam the planet, are killed by ship strikes at an alarming rate. In September 2007 Dr. Frances Gulland assisted with the examination of a dead blue whale in Ventura County and found hemorrhages and fractured vertebrae. This was the third blue whale in two weeks to wash up on the shores of Southern California, compared with only five blue whales that had washed up in the same region in the previous twenty-four years.

Once hunted to near extinction, the population has slowly climbed back to 1 percent of its former numbers, since the International Whaling Commission banned blue whale hunting in 1966. Blue whales have long periods of juvenile dependency, require much maternal care, and live long lives. Their regeneration time is slow. The blue whale population can't afford a sudden increase in ship strikes.

ABOVE: Blue whales can live up to 120 years. Pregnancy lasts eleven months and is followed by seven months of nursing. Killing a female can have long-lasting repercussions. This whale was found with contusions and broken vertebrae consistent with being hit by a ship.

chapter 3

IN 1998 THE MARINE MAMMAL CENTER WAS OVERRUN.
There had been 1,123 animals admitted that year, up from
628 the year before. Rescue volunteers worked around
the clock, like an ambulance crew in a war zone, unload-
ing sea mammals from their trucks, then rushing back
out to the next call. The Center's dispatchers couldn't
find enough rescuers to keep up with the incoming calls.

"All of us have in our veins the exact same percentage of salt in our blood that exists in the ocean . . . we have salt in our blood, in our sweat, in our tears. We are tied to the ocean. And when we go back to the sea . . . we are going back from whence we came."

—*John F. Kennedy, 1962*

THE LOGBOOK

Volunteers and staff must cultivate a sublime state of emotional discipline to survive at the Marine Mammal Center. They must rescue these animals, and they must euthanize many of them. They must care for these animals, but not bond with them, or the animals will never be wild again. Every new patient must be approached with a renewed sense of hope.

The night crew, who work from 6 PM to 2 AM beneath the stars to the sounds of the waves and seal calls, have kept an informal logbook since 1992. Filled with photos, cartoons, origami seals, and candid essays, it's served as a group diary for more than a decade. Kept private until now, it's a rare look into the private inner world of the Center's volunteers. Posted on the inside front cover and written in 1994, with no author attribution, is the following:

Coping with Death:
Rescue, rehabilitation, and release.
These are the motivations which
impel us to work resolutely and tire-
lessly every week. For nurturing and
caring for a pinniped by our own
hands and returning it to its natural
habitat as a healthy being gives us
a source of strength and a closer

connection to nature. However, not every seal makes it to the release stage. Indeed, about forty percent of the animals that we take in die at the Center. In order for us to be better prepared and better able to cope with this fact, let us pledge ourselves to the following:

The ten spiritual steps that follow address the inner struggle to act with tireless compassion without submitting to grief. It ends:

Witnessing our seals and sea lions die can be difficult. But we have the fortitude and the resources to contend with death, for if we are to continue our work, we must.

PAGE 47: Sea otters are one of the few animals that use tools. They hammer clamshells against stones balanced on their bellies to crack them open.

OPPOSITE, TOP: Northern fur seal pups are feisty, yet die at alarming rates. "Tough and fragile at the same time," is how one volunteer described them. As of 2009, northern fur seal birthrates have declined to their lowest since 1916. **OPPOSITE, BOTTOM:** A night crew volunteer offers fish to an orphan harbor seal pup. It is fitted with a temporary satellite tag, as it will soon be released.

Sea lions were arriving in record numbers, many of them wracked with seizures. Most of them were adult females, many pregnant. Soon the pen floors were littered with miscarried fetuses. Mothers who gave birth to viable young attacked them while the umbilical cord was still attached. The marine mammal hospital was overloaded with so many patients that the animals were grouped in pens designed for single animals. The nursing staff of volunteers had to step over them to administer anti-seizure medication and take blood samples, frequently slipping on blood, feces, and amniotic fluid and hoping not to land on a patient.

Seventy sea lions died in one weekend. Harbor seals fared no better: A staggering 85 percent died that year due to malnutrition, bacterial infections, and a herpes virus outbreak.

Sailors in Monterey Bay began to wonder why they were bumping into such a glut of floating logs. When they would look over the sides of their boats, they would discover that the "logs" were actually the bodies of sea lions.

Volunteers remember looking out at the calm blue ocean from their commanding view at the Center and thinking, "What is going on out there?"

Beneath that placid surface, something terrible was happening.

A rapid scan of the history of the animals' symptoms compared to those of humans unearthed a disturbing precedent. In 1987 three Canadians died and about a hundred were sickened on Prince Edward Island after eating mussels. Nineteen of the afflicted who were rushed to the hospital showed a distinct pattern of symptoms: seizures, catatonia, and coma. Some victims were admitted to nursing homes with permanent short-term memory loss. Residents thus called it "amnesiac shellfish poisoning."

Dr. Gulland knew that a true scientific approach to determining the cause of the 1998 epidemic required information on sea lion natural history, ecology, and their environment, which couldn't be rapidly achieved without collaboration from specialists around the country. Contemplating the scale of the crisis, Gulland realized that the only way to get answers was to lead an emergency scientific discovery project in rapid turnaround time.

The Center didn't have millions of dollars or high-tech facilities in 1998, but did have the support of the U.S. National Marine Fisheries Service, which had an emergency fund for responding to unusual marine mammal mortality events. The Center had a vast database of blood and serum samples ranging back twenty-three years and detailed records of almost ten

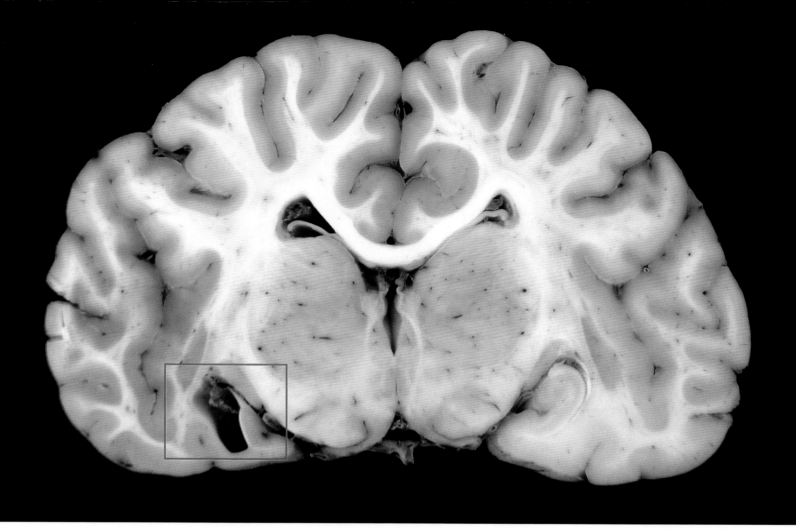

ABOVE: Domoic acid poisoning causes shrinking of the hippocampus in the brain. The area marked above should be filled with the hippocampus like the right half.

thousand animals' symptoms, diagnoses, and success rates. They had the respect of scientific establishments from all over the world and a crack team of volunteers driven by phenomenal dedication and enthusiasm. And at that very moment, they were bringing in afflicted sea lions by the dozen. Who better to spearhead the fact-finding mission but themselves?

In a tour de force of collaboration with the School of Veterinary Medicine at U.C. Davis, U.C. Santa Cruz, NOAA, the National Marine Fisheries Service, the Moss Landing Marine Laboratories, and the Monterey Bay Aquarium Research Institute, the Center recruited a national network of pathologists, biochemists, epidemiologists, neurologists, marine biologists, and other specialists. Correlating so much data that the list of authors would be paragraphs-long, Gulland and her colleagues published a series of findings in short order; one paper

found its way into the world-respected journal *Nature*. They concluded:

- Sea lion seizures are caused by exposure to domoic acid, a natural by-product of some species of diatoms, which are single-celled algae with glass-like shells in the genus *Pseudo-nitzschia*. Distinct traces of the biotoxin were found in the blood, urine, and feces of afflicted animals.

- Domoic acid can cause seizures and brain damage in marine mammals, birds, and humans.
- Domoic acid crosses the placental barrier. Domoic acid was found in the urine of miscarried sea lion fetuses.
- Fetal exposure to domoic acid at very low doses could cause epilepsy and unstable behavior that does not manifest until later in life.

ABOVE: Healthy sea lions don't drink water. They get all the freshwater they need by eating fish. Freshwater drinking is a likely sign that this young California sea lion is suffering from leptospirosis, a kidney disease that can be lethal.

"Because of the Center's research, governmental warnings were issued and certain fish were removed from stores."

BELOW: In one Coastal Cleanup Day alone, more than sixty thousand volunteers collected more than nine hundred thousand pounds of trash from our beaches, lakes, and waterways.

OPPOSITE: This resting male California sea lion bears the marks of a rough-and-tumble lifestyle.

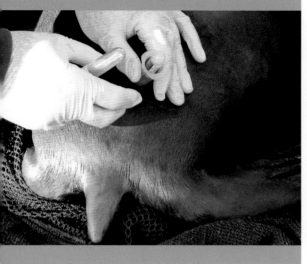

TOP: The Center's vast database of blood samples provides crucial information shared with marine biologists worldwide. **BOTTOM:** Dr. Frances Gulland leads a necropsy to determine how this blue whale died so that future deaths can be prevented.

Dr. Gulland reported that between 1998 and 2008, "seven hundred of the three thousand stranded California sea lions processed by the Marine Mammal Center have demonstrated neurological and behavioral symptoms strongly linked with domoic acid exposure. Prior to 1998, such symptoms in stranded sea lions were extremely rare."

But if domoic acid has always been a toxic by-product of a natural microbe, why hadn't the marine mammal hospital seen domoic acid poisoning before? What caused the toxic plague in the first place? Were these harmful algal blooms increasing?

Domoic acid is a neurotoxin that occurs naturally in the marine environment; it's been a natural by-product of the algae *Pseudo-nitzschia* since the time before bears took to the water and became seals and sea lions. The subtle neurological compass that allows marine mammals to migrate hundreds of miles to breed and feed and to pinpoint a fast-flitting fish at the black bottom of the ocean is destroyed by this once-rare ocean poison.

Sea lions treated for domoic acid poisoning and nursed back to vitality have been released into the oceans with satellite-linked transmitters so that their locations could be monitored. One swam straight toward Hawaii and was never heard from again, a strange behavior for an animal specialized for coastal living. In behavior reminiscent of

Humphrey, Delta, and Dawn, others have swam in the opposite direction: up estuaries and through culverts, many climbing out of drainage ditches and walking far inland through towns. One such sea lion, named Chippy, found warmth on the hood of a highway patrol car.

Gulland's research team showed that an animal exposed to a high level of domoic acid for a short time is better off than an animal exposed to a small level of domoic acid over a longer period of time. Acute cases can recover. Flushing the body fluids and administering antiseizure medicine can save the animal before debilitating brain damage occurs. But repeated chronic exposure causes long-term brain damage that is not curable, and virtually all chronic cases are euthanized to prevent a slower, painful death.

Since intensive monitoring began in 1998, algal blooms producing domoic acid appear to be becoming more frequent. The cause? Several factors are important. *Pseudo-nitzschia's* favorite foods are the same nutrients that nourish suburban lawns and rural farms: nitrates, phosphorus, urea, and iron—otherwise known as fertilizer. Every day, billions of gallons of human waste flow into the oceans. Sewage treatment plants eliminate most of the disease-causing bacteria but have little effect on the outpouring of nutrients that toxic algae feed on.

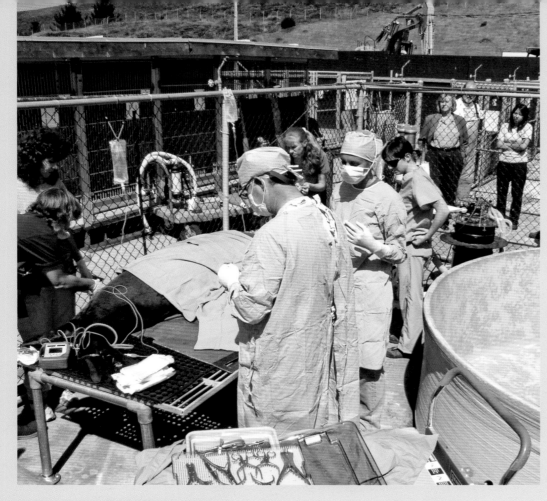

DAILY PATIENT ROUNDS

Sitting at a round table in the triage room are a dozen veterinarians, vet techs, biologists, and senior volunteers. Husbandry manager Deb Wickham is standing by the wall charts that monitor each animal's progress. She pages through a clipboard as she addresses her audience.

"Chompy didn't want to eat today. But he gained weight yesterday. So we're giving him some more time. Archie is in for eye surgery Thursday. Fuzzi Buzzi has an infected flipper. He's skinny, but gained four kilos so far. Fenway wants to leave, but he still has a high white blood cell count."

A giant grin spreads over Dr. Frances Gulland's face. Now and then she allows herself to lose her scientific objectivity in a sudden burst of affection for an animal. "He wants to leave?"

"When we latch the pens, he watches very closely," Wickham deadpans.

It's a good sign. Sea lions are so intelligent, they can figure out how to unlatch pens, so bungee cords are required. Long-term patients wheeled in and out of pens make a point of looking for escape routes and memorizing the grounds, as if planning a breakout.

The veterinary scientist in Gulland returns. "When his white blood count is down, schedule a release for Fenway," she says. "What's the diagnosis on Bosco?"

Faces fall.

"Drugs are not calming him," says Wickham. "He's got abrasions on his front flippers and nose from convulsions he must have acquired before stranding on the beach. Looks like long-term effects of previous exposure."

Gulland swallows. The vet techs are all too familiar with these symptoms.

"I'm going to give him the shot and let him sleep for ten minutes," says Gulland. "Then we give him fifteen ccs of sodium pentobarbital."

That's a lethal dose of the anesthetic. Gulland turns to Denise Greig, a marine biologist, who returns a sad smile that they've shared many times before. "Are you available to help me with the necropsy in a half hour?"

"Sure," Greig replies.

ABOVE LEFT: When the animals are too large to be brought into the surgery room, the surgery room is brought to the animal.

"Healing all the sea lions, seals, otters, and porpoises in the world isn't good enough if we send them back out into a sick ocean."

ABOVE: A Northern elephant seal mother naps with two pups.

OPPOSITE: A male Northern elephant seal with a battle-scarred chest and a long nose called a proboscis contemplates his next move with a female.

ABOVE: Participating in Coastal Cleanup Day is a great way to meet kindred spirits. **CENTER:** To some, the pollution problem may seem insurmountable. But if our collective carelessness created the trash, our collective care can clean it up.

All over the world, as humans move to the coasts, freshwater runoff from urban areas is contributing to the ascendancy of the microbe. Oceanographers describe this as an oceanwide return to the primordial soup. In the mass die-offs of multicellular plants and animals, and in the necrosis of brains at the top of the food chain, we are witnessing an environmental imbalance that affects the simplest life to the most complex.

The Marine Mammal Center organized this discovery project in the nick of time. Although it was well known that domoic acid could accumulate in seafood, the effects on the mammals eating them were poorly understood. Marine mammals, which eat a lot more fish than humans do, suffer the symptoms before humans do. Dr. Gulland, who led the research team that discovered the cause of brain damage in sea lions, explains it to anyone who will

listen: "Sea lions eat the same foods we do, but more of them—foods like anchovies, squid, and salmon. We may see the effects of domoic acid in them before we see it in people. Sea lions may be an early warning sign for humans."

Because of the Marine Mammal Center's research, governmental warnings were issued and certain fish were removed from stores. But despite these measures, poor fishermen still subsist on toxic fish caught from waters recognized as Environmental Protection Agency Superfund sites.

Dr. Gulland speaks to any visitor with an earnestness that urges, *You can do something about this*. Healing all the sea lions, seals, otters, and porpoises in the world isn't good enough if we send them back out into a sick ocean. All the Center's work is for naught if the world doesn't understand and change. So she starts explaining, one person at a time.

ABOVE: California Coastal Cleanup Day earned a mention in *The Guinness Book of World Records*. Since 1985, more than eight hundred thousand Californians have removed more than twelve million pounds of debris from the state's shorelines and coast.

THANKS FOR THE HEADS-UP, LITTLE GUY

- Northern fur seal pups knew about El Niño before we did. In the fall of 1997, record numbers of malnourished pups showed up on beaches, alerting humans of drastic climate changes.

- Sea lions with cancer have high levels of PCB (a toxic environmental pollutant) and DDT (a pesticide) in their blubber. DDT was banned from America in 1973, and PCBs were banned in 1988, but the contaminants are still present in coastal waters and marine mammal bloodstreams. "Human activities are knocking things out of balance," says Andrew Dobson of Princeton University. "For some pathogens, we're seeing nasty synergistic effects with contaminants, such as PCBs."

ABOVE: Northern fur seal pups learn the ins and outs of their new environment quickly.

OPPOSITE: Two Hawaiian monk seals spoon contentedly.

RELEASE

A volunteer backs the Center's truck onto the narrow beach at Fitzgerald Marine Reserve, Moss Beach, in San Mateo County for a routine release of a juvenile sea lion. Seven members of the public happen to be standing around—two from Nebraska, three from Israel, and two locals. As he unloads the heavy crate off his truck, visitors can't believe their luck—a live seal!

"Not technically a seal," says the volunteer. "This is a sea lion. He's got ears and he walks on all fours. You'll see when I let him out."

They pepper him with questions while he works. He never tires of answering questions. He knows these innocent bystanders

are about to experience the same feeling that drives him to volunteer. He opens the crate. Out waddles a juvenile sea lion.

"Awwww, how cute!" squeals the lady from Nebraska. "What's his name?"

"Bronco."

"Why do you call him Bronco— *AAAAHH!*"

Bystanders retreat in panic as Bronco fakes a bluff charge, barking, his teeth displayed. The volunteer is in place to block Bronco with a rescue board, but it's a perfunctory gesture. He knows this is just a sea lion's show of intimidation.

Snorting with satisfaction that he is the alpha juvenile of the beach, Bronco turns and waddles over the rocks, then dives into the waves. His transformation from humorous awkwardness on land to supple grace in the ocean is so astonishing, it silences the nervous laughter. Bronco swims off without so much as a sensitive glance over his shoulder. You get the sense he never wants to see another person with a rescue board for as long as he lives. He's returned to the place where he doesn't have a name.

Something happens among the quiet humans. You can't describe it, but you can feel it: a current among eight strangers and friends, an experience always sought but rarely attained—a profound and shared sense of meaning.

OPPOSITE, TOP: Sea lions, who walk on all four flippers, can leap off a truck. **OPPOSITE, BOTTOM:** Seals, who crawl on their bellies, must be released on the ground.

ABOVE: Healthy sea lions are released back into the wild. **LEFT:** Schoolchildren observe while four volunteers with herding boards coax a rehabilitated male sea lion out to sea.

"The one process now going on that will take millions of years to correct is the loss of genetic and species diversity by the destruction of natural habitats. This is the folly our descendants are least likely to forgive us."

—*Edward O. Wilson*, Biophilia, *1984*

chapter 4

THE ORIGINAL MISSION OF THE MARINE MAMMAL CENTER was to heal sick animals and conduct scientific research. But the scientific research was showing that restoring animals to health did little good if they are released into an ailing sea. Some animals released into the wild vigorous and healthy return to the hospital two and three times.

There is no way around it: Marine mammal suffering is connected to ocean health. Ocean health is connected to our daily choices. Daily choices—and how to make them to benefit our marine environment—therefore became another focus of the Center.

To accomplish its mission, the Center needs a healthy environment in which to release its patients. The Center realized that an ocean environment would never become healthy without a more intensive education platform—one

Whale Bus™

Marine Science Outreach Program
(415) 289-7330

PAGE 64: A male California sea lion returns to the ocean with a temporary satellite tag that will chart his progress in the wild.

ABOVE: The popular Whale Bus program makes learning fun. Approximately 20 percent of the schoolchildren taught by the Center are from inner-city backgrounds.

as ambitious as the scientific discovery project that proved that domoic acid was the cause of brain damage. With all its support, talent, and commitment, the Center couldn't heal sick animals alone. It needed to inform the public. It needed a new generation of environmental stewards.

Schoolchildren took their first class trips to the California Marine Mammal Center in 1976, a year after the Center was founded. Since then, Center educators have taught tens of thousands of children at the hospital on field trips, at local schools, and at Rodeo Beach. They have also conducted summer day camps, led trips to local tide pools, and guided excursions from land at Point Reyes to watch the annual gray whale

migration, yet the programs taught at the hospital are by far the most popular. Seeing live marine mammals up close, hearing their sounds, observing tube feedings and medical procedures, and seeing the wounds from entanglements are truly unique experiences only found at the Marine Mammal Center. By 1993 the numbers looked impressive: A total of 905 programs had been conducted, with 620 of those programs taught at the Center, serving more than twenty-five thousand students.

But in the face of the Center's research findings on the domoic acid outbreak of 1998, twenty-five thousand informed students suddenly seemed like a drop in the bucket. With urban coastal development

wreaking such deep, systematic havoc on marine environments, the core mission of education was all the more important. Publishing scientific contributions was the first step. And the problem wasn't just in the Bay Area. The poisoning of coastal waters was global. "Dead zones" were appearing off the coasts of major cities on every continent. Even saving just the California coastline would never be enough. But how to get the word out?

In 1998 the Center hit the streets in the Whale Bus. Instructors drove the van to Bay Area schools, bringing specimens such as pelts, bones, and whale baleen to teach classes about marine mammals and ocean conservation. In 1999, its first full year at the Center, the Whale Bus instructors taught more than four hundred programs. Today the Whale Bus continues to be a beloved program, teaching approximately twelve thousand students each year, with a special commitment to underserved schools.

In the beginning, the Whale Bus worked wonders for students from school districts with limited budgets, but the van couldn't make it to every school. In addition, the Center was located in a relatively remote outpost of the Marin Headlands. How could the Center bring itself to more underserved schoolchildren?

The plan was to make class trips to the Marine Mammal Center so much fun that

OVERFISHING

Overfishing has been disastrous not only to many species of marine mammals, but also to the fishing communities relying on the harvest. Overfishing can do more than endanger our food supply. Some scientists say it causes widespread changes in ocean ecology: degradation of reefs, destruction of bottom grasses, increased algal blooms. Many fishing methods are indiscriminate—that is, they pull many more unintended animals out of the sea than the specific fish they're targeting. The result is called by-catch, and it has an enormous impact on ocean ecosystems.

Ocean fish are the last wild creatures left that humans hunt on a large scale. If overfishing is controlled, ecosystems often recover.

ABOVE: These common dolphins travel together with hundreds of others. The middle dolphin has a remora (suckerfish) attached.

Volunteers do whatever it takes, whether it's sterilizing feeding tubes **(TOP)** or preparing the several formula recipes of fish mash **(BOTTOM)** designed for the nutritional needs of each species.

GIVING BACK

Alyssa Stark was a senior at Rancho Cotate High School in Rohnert Park when she heard that a biology class was going on a field trip. Stark wasn't even a member of the class, but she enjoyed field trips, so she tagged along, having no idea where she was going.

After one day touring the Marine Mammal Center, Stark realized what she wanted to do with her life. "I knew I wanted to be the person in those pens. In class, it's all so abstract," she says. "It's not a hands-on application of your knowledge. Somehow classroom biology never taught me that science could be applied to my love of animals."

After she graduated, Stark volunteered at the Center. She started out as green as you can get. The girl who was afraid of needles had the chance to draw blood from live animals and participate in necropsies. A favorite story among her old crew is the time Stark mistook a jacket on the floor for an escaped seal and tried to corral it with a herding board.

She didn't remain inexperienced for long. During the next seven years, Stark would work all her later schooling around volunteering. While she was a biology student at U.C. Davis, she would drive two hours to volunteer. When she was promoted to assistant supervisor, she often started her commute at 2 AM. Once she slept in her car so that she could work all night, then drive to school the next day.

"Volunteers feel valued here," she says. "The staff lets you know that without you, it can't happen."

Stark served in almost every capacity at the Center. She moved from animal care supervision to education. She was trained as a docent and instructor. She stood in booths at science fairs to instruct the public. She rescued stranded animals from the beach. She even worked in the gift shop. But the most gratifying task of all was teaching children the same way she had been taught.

Today Alyssa Stark is working on her PhD in biology and polymer science at the University of Akron, Ohio. Stark can't imagine what would have become of her if she had never attended that class trip.

"At the Marine Mammal Center, I learned confidence, how to supervise, how to lead, how to teach. I learned deductive reasoning, how science works. It's why I was accepted to multiple graduate programs. The Marine Mammal Center has given so much to me. I know that sounds weird considering I worked long hours for free, but I want to give back to them in a scientific way."

every student along the Center's 600-mile rescue range from northern to central California would clamor for it and so educational that every teacher would demand it. Major donors created a scholarship fund wherein 75 percent of the students who are brought to the Center under the aegis of this fund qualify for the AFDC Free and Reduced-Price Lunch Program. Approximately 20 percent of the students are from inner-city or rural backgrounds and might not otherwise be exposed to marine science and the ocean environment.

In the Call to the Rescue program, students participate in a mock rescue and rehabilitation of a seal using a stuffed animal and actual veterinary tools and techniques. The Guided Beach Walk program encourages students to learn about how the fascinating plants and animals washed ashore are adapted for life in the ocean; by collecting trash that litters the beach, students see the evidence of human effects on marine life. Research Discovery Day is a sophisticated program whereby high school and junior college students participate in labs in hematology, comparative anatomy, or radiology that replicate research done by real scientists.

Above and beyond this, the Marine Mammal Center offers hands-on learning for college biology students, rigorous internships for graduate students, and veterinary internship and externship programs for students learning veterinary medicine. With these programs at the Marine Mammal Center on their résumés, our future marine biologists and veterinarians are empowered to apply their passion for nature to a fruitful career.

The Center's Marine Science Discovery Program was designed specifically for underserved high school students in the Bay Area. At least three-quarters are people of color, and many have never seen the ocean or understood that they live close to a complex bay-delta estuary. Funded by a government grant and matching private donations, the eight-week program opens the eyes of high school students from disadvantaged backgrounds to the possibilities in marine science careers.

The first component of the program involves four classroom visits. Instructors from the Center arrive at the school to inform the students about the various careers in marine science—from teacher and biologist to boat captain or lab technician—including qualifications required, pay scales, and education and work experience for each profession. Students dissect fish and learn about the identification of "hard parts" (bones, scales, and eye lenses), including the otolith, or fish ear bone, for various species. The students then sift through dried sea lion scat looking for these hard parts to identify what the animal had eaten.

TOP: In the Marine Science Discovery Program, students collect samples along the shoreline. **BOTTOM:** High school students learn scientific techniques used by marine biologists during Research Discovery Day.

TOP: "Hands-on learning" is the motto of the Center's Marine Science Discovery Program, where students aboard *The Adventure Cat* sail the bay to collect samples. **BOTTOM:** Students learn to analyze X-rays and draw conclusions about a patient's diagnosis.

LEFT: Differences in skulls, jaws, and teeth among marine mammal species reflect adaptations to various diets. **BELOW:** Students learn in a cooperative, interactive atmosphere that fosters teamwork.

WHY ARE THE SEALS CRYING?

They're healthy! Unlike animals that live on land, seals have no internal tear ducts. When seals are on land, tears flow continuously to keep their eyes wet. When seals stop shedding tears, it means they're sick. So tears on a seal are good!

The next stage involves three field trips. Buses chartered by the Center deliver students to the hospital, where they are escorted on a behind-the-scenes tour, viewing seal and sea lion patients and learning about the diseases and conditions that bring them to the Center. In the marine science classroom, students participate in labs where they learn to analyze blood samples, compare marine mammal anatomy, and analyze X-rays. They hike from the beach to the hills to observe the behavior of a wild harbor seal colony. Students use scientific instruments for water-quality testing and sample the beach for a small crustacean called a sand crab. The day ends with a hillside hike, during which they can look across the bay and get a magnificent view of the great Golden Gate Bridge, where the bay-delta estuary meets the Pacific Ocean.

Finally, the students board a research and training vessel, the *White Holly*, a 138-foot retired coast guard buoy tender, and cruise the San Francisco Bay. While they sail beneath the Golden Gate Bridge, students collect water samples and determine salinity, temperature, and dissolved oxygen content. They record their location using a GPS device, participate in a plankton tow, and use a video microscope to identify microscopic plankton species, all the while filling out worksheets as they collect data.

A select few of the most motivated students are awarded a paid summer internship at the Marine Mammal Center.

At PIER 39's K-Dock in San Francisco, tourists can't resist the hundreds of sea lions that loll about every winter. Once their

curiosity is piqued, the Marine Mammal Center is there to answer questions. Since 1990 docents specially trained by the Center have taught school groups and the public about California sea lions' biology, behavior, and how they moved onto K-Dock in the first place. The Marine Mammal Interpretive Center and Store and its Education Kiosk at K-Dock are added bonuses that allow the curious to explore on their own. The Center's presence at the busy tourist spot allows docents to spread their message to visitors from around the world.

But little is as informative as the sea lions themselves. These mammals are a testament to the power of coexistence between humans and wildlife, and K-Dock has been declared a "Watchable Wildlife" viewing area by the California Watchable Wildlife Project. At PIER 39, humans and sea lions have worked out an unspoken arrangement: Sea lions sleep, swim, play, fight, and bark, entertaining the crowds while the docents educate.

Many sea lions are seen with trash and fishing net entanglements on their bodies. Since the sea lions took over K-Dock in 1989, more than seventy-five sick and injured sea lions have been rescued from the crowded and slippery dock. Few who see them forget them, and visitors from every continent return to their communities spreading the message of conservation.

REAL SCIENCE

In 2007 Oakland High School students participating in the Center's Marine Science Discovery Program made a significant contribution to science. When a tanker ship crashed into the San Francisco–Oakland Bay Bridge, spilling 58,000 gallons of its own fuel oil that washed up on beaches, scientists at the National Marine Sanctuary needed to assess the impact of the damage.

A researcher at U.C. Santa Barbara's Marine Science Institute had already established that sand crabs are a perfect bio-indicator species to gauge the effects of toxic releases on beach ecology. But the scientists needed baseline data on crabs *before* the oil spill happened. So they put out a call for any scientists who happened to have recently taken measurements. They found their answer in the students from Oakland High, who had surveyed the crabs at Rodeo Beach the day before the spill and dutifully turned over their data.

TOP: The Marine Science Discovery Program is a "hands-on, feet-wet" experience. **BOTTOM:** Rodeo Beach, located just below the Marine Mammal Center, is known for its "rainbow sand."

TOP AND BOTTOM: Schoolchildren participate in a mock "call to the rescue," in which they learn every step of capture, transport, assessment, and medical care.

OPPOSITE: Ann Bauer teaches a class at Rodeo Beach.

CALL TO THE RESCUE

Ms. Barone's special education fourth through sixth grade class from Murphy Elementary in Richmond, California, are sitting on a long log on Rodeo Beach as Ann Bauer, director of education at the Center, is concluding her lecture on how to tell seals from sea lions and the safe use of nets and herding boards.

All of a sudden her radio crackles. "Hang on," she tells the class, "I have a call from our rescue coordinator. Yes?"

"Ann, we got a report of a seal stranded on Rodeo Beach," says a dispatcher. "Can you see if it is still there, assess the situation, and call back?"

Bauer speaks into her radio, "I'm just starting a program at the beach. If it's okay with the teacher, we could locate the animal. I do have some rescue gear we use in the program, and I could leave it at the bridge."

Ms. Barone nods. Bauer sheathes her radio into her holster. "This is a great opportunity! We have time to look for the seal and incorporate that in the program."

The students are excited. Bauer reminds them that if they are to look for a seal, they must be quiet or the seal will be frightened back into the ocean. She calls for volunteer schoolchildren to grab the net, crate, and herding boards. Students march in silent formation, brows furrowed with concern and professionalism, each creeping silently so as not to scare the seal away.

They're participating in the Call to the Rescue education program. At the Marine Mammal Center, the volunteers learn by doing, and so do the students. They search the beach until an alert child shouts and points. A harbor seal stuffed animal is hiding beneath the bridge a few feet from the water. As the group arrives, the first students see the seal and realize it's a toy, while the others arrive still excited and hoping to see a real seal.

The children look at the seal, which does not react.

"It's a seal pup with a plastic strap on its neck!" says Bauer. "If we do not get that plastic off, it will cut its neck. The wound will bleed and get infected, or it could make it hard to swallow food, or he could choke to death. We've got to get him to the hospital! But he's facing the water!" shouts Bauer. "He could make a break for it at any second, and we could lose him!"

Bauer shouts to two girls with herding boards, "Head him off, boarders!"

The two girls with herding boards half-heartedly move into position between the seal and the water.

"Not like that! Did you forget your training? What if he goes for the water?"

Bauer grabs the seal and moves it quickly toward the water. The boarders race to block the seal. "Quick! That way!" Bauer feints left with such alacrity that the girls with boards collide, but they block the seal. "Good job. He's not able to reach the water." Bauer cuts right with the stuffed harbor seal, but the girls with boards have got their blocking technique down.

"They got him blocked! Net boy! Bring the net! Bring it down on him! Quick!"

A boy has been waiting with the over-size net at the ready. He charges forward and swings the net down hard on the stuffed animal—*crack!*—right onto Bauer's head.

Bauer doesn't miss a beat. "I'm okay! We've got to save the seal!"

She drops the stuffed animal and leaps away. "The seal is pausing for a breath! Nab him!" The boy lowers the net in a perfectly executed capture.

Bauer shows the students how to safely restrain and move the stuffed seal into a cage without being bitten. The students carry the caged seal and rescue gear to the marine science classroom, where they learn how to take blood from a seal and to tube-feed the stuffed animal. The students are instructed on how to ask the questions marine mammal veterinarians routinely ask and how to fill out the seal's medical chart as they make steps toward a diagnosis.

Blood, urine, and fecal samples are discussed. One of the students ventures a

diagnosis, "A harbor seal pup that should still be with its mom . . ."

Another student chimes in, "It had a plastic strap, like ones that come on boxes of paper, on its neck."

Using blunt surgical scissors, a ten-year-old gingerly cuts the entanglement off the patient's neck. Bauer explains why they did not cut the plastic strap off on the beach. Since the animal was breathing, it was best to transport it to the hospital and cut the entanglement off in a sterile environment with the tools needed to clean the wound, stop blood flow, and, if needed, stitch the wound closed. The students then fit the seal with a flipper tag and leave it to rest.

"In the **marine science classroom**, students participate in labs where they learn to **analyze blood samples**, compare marine mammal anatomy, and analyze X-rays."

BELOW: A sea otter pup rests on her mother while they share a snack.

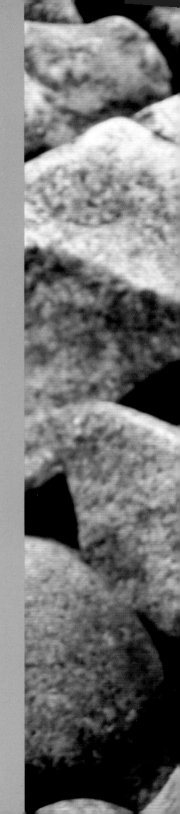

chapter 5

WITH SUCCESS CAME NEW CHALLENGES. By 2005 the Marine Mammal Center was recognized as one of the premier marine mammal hospitals in the world. Its commitment to environmental sustainability was recognized that year with Senator Barbara Boxer's Conservation Champion Award. The senator called the Center "the jewel in the crown" of California's conservation programs.

But its physical facilities had not kept up with either its advances or its reputation. Visiting scholars, fellows, PhD students, and externs from all over the world who flew in to learn techniques from the Center were often surprised that the staff and volunteers were able to treat so many animals with such cobbled-together facilities. Dr. Frances Gulland, whose papers they had read, conducted her research from semipermanent trailers used as offices. Five of the seven

"Never doubt that a **small group** of thoughtful, committed citizens **can change the world**. Indeed, it is the only thing that ever has."

—*Margaret Mead, cultural anthropologist*

PAGE 79: This young sea lion pup takes a break from the water on a rocky stretch of coastline.

ABOVE: The facilities, finished in the summer of 2009, are a model of environmental sustainability. **CENTER:** Construction of the Marine Mammal Center's new building began in earnest in November 2005 after thirty thousand members and donors pledged to support a facility worthy of the work.

buildings were converted freight containers, some more than twenty years old. The water-filtration system was strung together with aboveground polyvinyl pipes, which were eroding. The hospital had no public restrooms, just two Porta Potties, and very minimal signage. The classroom was a twelve-minute walk from the hospital. Instructors taught four hundred classes a year, mostly outdoors. When it rained, instructors had to clear the garage of rescue vehicles and sweep off the bleachers so students could sit; then the instructors transported their teaching materials in Rubbermaid crates and set them up on old rusty tables.

The outmoded facilities could no longer support the work. Time that should have been spent on research and animal care was diverted to fixing outdated equipment and temporary structures. Every hour spent fixing a pool ramp was an hour taken away from the care of a sick animal that might be suffering a few feet away. Every dollar spent replacing a rusty pipe was a dollar taken away from research that would save animals in the future. Donors and members agreed it was time to build a permanent facility worthy of its patients.

Today the state-of-the-art facility brings all of the necessary functions for marine mammal diagnosis, treatment, research, and education to one site. This streamlines the work of every department, which increases the speed and efficiency of each process. The potential for advances in research is incalculable, to say nothing of

The Marine Mammal Center's rescue range extends along an incredible 600 miles of central and northern California coastline, from northern San Luis Obispo through southern Mendocino counties. Field offices are located in San Luis Obispo, Monterey, and Mendocino counties, and together with volunteers and staff at the hospital, their staff has treated more than twelve thousand California sea lions, elephant seals, harbor seals, porpoises, and other marine mammals. The Center relies heavily on its volunteers living in each part of its range to assess stranded animals, rescue them if necessary, provide triage and emergency care, and transport the animals using a relay system to the full-service veterinary hospital in Sausalito. Through the coordinated efforts of a vastly distributed team, the Marine Mammal Center personnel work to perfect the cycle of rapid response, rescue, rehabilitation, and release.

ABOVE: Solar panels provide electric power for the facility while offering shade for the animal pens.

the increased safety of the volunteers and staff, the comfort and survivability of the animals, and visibility to the public.

The Center's commitment to environmental sustainability is visible in almost every detail of its construction. Acoustic ceiling panels are made out of compressed seaweed. The walls and insulation are made out of recycled paper and glue. A radiant floor-heating system heats the buildings. Skylights bathe the Center in natural light from the sun, so less electricity is used. Photovoltaic panels above the pens provide shade for the animals and will decrease the Center's energy use by about 10 percent, enough to power between five and seven houses. The grounds are landscaped with native plants that do not require irrigation. Even the parking lot

VOLUNTEERING LOOKS GREAT ON YOUR RÉSUMÉ

Many volunteers swear that they learned their most crucial skills while volunteering at the Marine Mammal Center. Volunteers in administration learn how to fund-raise, apply for grants, market, and raise public awareness. Supervisors learn how to manage a team, lead, and motivate. Docents learn how to educate the public and teach every level of student, from grade-schoolers to adults. Youth volunteers, ages fourteen to seventeen, gain self-confidence and learn responsibility as team players working side by side with adults. And if you want to become a scientist, volunteering at the Center looks as good on your résumé and school applications as just about any diploma or employer recommendation.

ABOVE: In the spring, volunteers prepare many individual portions of elephant seal pup formula for orphans.

concrete is pervious, allowing rainwater to seep into the ground instead of channeling toward the sea.

One of the two original missile silos on the site houses the animals' Life Support System. This state-of-the-art water-treatment system has the capacity to hold at least 250,000 gallons of water and to recycle much of the water in the patient pools. The water-treatment system drains and replaces the water in each pool every fifteen minutes. Maintained two stories below grade, its location allows for greater efficiency and keeps the animals' water source safe.

With the infrastructure to work at optimum efficiency, the Center is poised to tackle its most difficult challenge yet.

Here's what science has taught us: The health of marine mammals requires a healthy marine environment. The health of the marine environment depends on the cumulative effects of our daily choices.

Nothing so empowers people to change as when a scientific conclusion matches a conviction of the heart. If the Marine Mammal Center is to fulfill its mission, the daily choices of millions of individuals must change. Suffering sea lions highlight the potential fate of humans. Our sentinels of the sea have taught us through their suffering. Their seizures, brain damage, and death might have been ours.

The oceans remain a deep mystery for scientists and poets alike. The best indicator of ocean health is the vitality of its top predators, which are intelligent mammals like sea lions, seals, whales, porpoises, and humans. Sea lions and seals are content to live within proximity of us. They need nothing to flourish except the waters they have called home for millions of years.

The Marine Mammal Center, at its essence, is an experiment in human nature. Its steady growth from three volunteers with an idea and a bathtub to a premier marine mammal research hospital has proven that, when the right motives attract the best minds and hearts to a cause, people can work together to exceed the founders' wildest dreams. Whether dislodging a live 40-ton whale from a drainage ditch 70 miles inland and returning him to the sea, or attracting some of the most talented administrators and veterinarians who forgo comfortable salaries and heated offices to work with inspired volunteers, or leading a worldwide discovery project to find the cause of sea lion seizures in a microscopic organism, or asking donors to contribute $30 million to build a new facility, the staff and volunteers at the Center have learned that, when the only motive is curiosity and compassion, thousands of people will rally to help.

As the Marine Mammal Center has grown in influence, it has connected to other institutions and people who have independently dedicated themselves to the same values of conservation. The trajectory of growth suggests that a passion for environmental stewardship will overtake the world in time to save the most intelligent creatures in the sea.

Imagine a new generation of world citizens who conduct their daily lives with an intimate awareness of how their mundane choices affect marine mammals and the oceans. This generation would share a set of modern values that transcends tribal boundaries. Young people speaking a hundred languages would share one voice, articulating the same scientifically informed system of beliefs: that human beings are animals who must live in harmony with the environment that nourishes all life.

If you get a chance to talk to any volunteer or staff member at the Marine Mammal Center, you'll find that each has already joined this generation and believes that a sense of global responsibility will continue to spread simply because it's the right thing to do. If enough of us join this generation of responsibility, the sea change in our consciousness may foster a change in the seas.

ABOVE: Merrill L. Magowan and Richard Vance transport an elephant seal to the scale.

OPPOSITE: At the Midway Atoll, experts visiting from the Marine Mammal Center and collaborators feed endangered Hawaiian monk seals a high-fat diet to prepare them to breed in the wild.

LEFT: Students inspect a pinniped skull in dentition class. **BELOW:** Dolphins are often considered an "indicator species," meaning they are the first to suffer from pollution. Many dolphin populations carry heavy loads of chemical contaminants.

"The best indicator of **ocean health** is the *vitality* of its top predators, which are **intelligent** mammals."

BELOW: Sea otters must eat as much as one-third of their weight each day to maintain their body heat.

OPPOSITE: Endangered Hawaiian monk seals are the only pinnipeds that live in warm, subtropical seas. Many juveniles are starving and marine biologists are working to understand why.

"While we are clearly an organization focused on marine mammals, we're also about people; the people who comprise our volunteer force, those who are part of our donor community, our board of directors, and, of course, our staff; passionate and committed people who channel their desire to make a difference through the Center. The connections we make among people and animals extend to the connections science has revealed between marine mammal health, the health of our oceans, and our own health. If we share the amazing stories of our patients, we'll create a more informed and passionate generation of stewards.

"Challenges to ocean health are enormous but the Marine Mammal Center community shows that if a few thousand people can make such a huge difference here, millions can make a difference in the world. All we need to do is spread the word."

—*Jeff Boehm, executive director of the Marine Mammal Center*

TOP: This 44.5-pound juvenile loggerhead sea turtle was named Shotgun because it rode "shotgun" in the rescue vehicle. **BOTTOM:** Volunteers scrub the pen floors with a disinfecting solution at least twice a day.

THE SPIRIT OF VOLUNTEERS

Volunteers, by definition, can't be bossed around. Volunteers must be self-motivated. This creates a subculture of dedication, loyalty, and respect that paying companies can only dream of. Ranging in age from fourteen to ninety, more than eight hundred volunteers handle everything from cleaning pens to preparing food, updating medical charts, administering antibiotics, and taking blood samples. Nearly 90 percent of the volunteers are women, but the animal hospital is not exactly the picture of femininity: Fish heads, blood, rubber boots, plastic pants, suspenders, flies, and the occasional necropsy are all part of the routine. The volunteers work outside, often in cold, windy, or wet weather, late at night and early in the morning. They see ugly wounds, emaciated animals, and sometimes must endure the loss of a favorite patient that they had labored to save. Yet the camaraderie and mutual respect never falters.

Each year the volunteers rack up more than eighty thousand hours at the Center. Most work as members of an animal care crew, which requires a commitment of eight or more hours per week. Some drive two-hour commutes for the opportunity to clean seal pens. If the Center had to pay professionals to get these jobs done, Merrill Magowan, chairman of the board of directors, estimates that it would cost hundreds of thousands of dollars every year.

When asked why they commit so much time and labor to such challenging work, volunteers tend to be tight-lipped, as if taking credit would taint the mission. They let their actions speak for them.

LEFT: This Steller sea lion was rescued as a pup. Steller sea lions are an endangered species. **TOP:** Young northern elephant seals spar and practice fighting for future battles for dominance. **BOTTOM:** The Wednesday day crew is connected by a shared devotion to a common goal.

WHAT YOU CAN DO TO PROTECT MARINE MAMMALS AND OUR SHARED OCEAN ENVIRONMENT

- An area of trash—most of it plastics—twice the size of Texas is swirling in the North Pacific Ocean. Drastically reduce your use of plastic bottles and other single-use disposable items.

- Plastic debris entangles many seals and sea lions that come to the Center. Please consider limiting your use of plastic grocery bags.

- Tools of convenience for us become remarkably effective snares for wildlife. Cut plastic six-pack rings with scissors, then put them in a recycling bin.

- Take ownership in the environment we share with marine mammals. Clean a beach, street, or park.

- Sustainable fisheries help sustain marine mammal populations. Use a sustainable seafood card when selecting

fish and shellfish for your meals. Check out "Seafood Watch" on the Monterey Bay Aquarium's Web site.

- Every action you take makes a difference for conservation—for better or worse. Perhaps nothing makes a more immediate impact than working directly with injured or ill seals and sea lions. Volunteer at the Marine Mammal Center!

- The Marine Mammal Center relies on the generous support of people who care enough to make a difference. Make a financial contribution to the Marine Mammal Center.

- Use your voice with the children in your life. Teach the next generation the values of an environmentally sustainable lifestyle. They are the ones who will fulfill our mission.

ABOVE: The Marine Mammal Center's commitment extends beyond the hospital—to our waterways, communities, schools, and the ocean environment we share with wild animals.

frequently asked questions

Q Sea lions and harbor seals are not technically endangered, so why save them?

A The information that the Marine Mammal Center has collected from working with healthy populations of marine mammals has been applied directly to species near extinction. For instance, the Hawaiian monk seal is considered the most endangered species in U.S. waters, with only about 1,100 left, and the population is declining at a rate of 4 percent per year. Yet scientists could not collect enough information from the tiny population to develop techniques to increase birthrates.

Hawaiian monk seal experts consulted directly with the Center for help. With experience in the care of thousands of elephant and harbor pups, the Center had developed techniques and health care models that were directly applicable to this species. In May 2006 the Center embarked on a joint conservation project at Midway Atoll, a U.S. territory near the Hawaiian Islands. Seven female juveniles, including a set of twins, were held in beach pens and fed a high-fat diet and nutritional supplements to help them fatten up for breeding.

When the endangered seals became sick, more advanced medical care learned at the Center was applied.

The twins, as well as four more females, were successfully released from Midway Atoll in March 2007. Encouraged, NOAA incorporated what was learned from this work into its Hawaiian monk seal recovery plan, released that summer. The pilot program offered renewed hope for the preservation of this species, but much more work needs to be done to prevent extinction. Knowing this, the Center dispatched teams of vets and volunteers to Hawaii from May to December 2008 to care for another orphaned monk seal pup named KP2 (released in December 2008!) and to learn as much as they could about the species.

The only task more important than saving individual animals is the information collected that can save whole populations. The best way to learn about endangered species is to collect information from their closest relatives. Just as we learn much about human health by examining our close cousin, the rat, invaluable information has been learned about endangered marine mammals through the Center's work with more populous species.

TOP: The only nonmammalian species to be treated at the Center, sea turtles that swim too far north must be treated for hypothermia and released into warmer waters in Southern California. **BOTTOM:** Adult male sea lions hold a breeding territory on rookeries for six weeks.

OPPOSITE: California sea lion pups stay with their mothers for six to nine months.

Q Aren't you just interfering with nature?

A Entanglements, overfishing of primary food sources, and nitrate runoff were never part of the marine mammal's natural environment. Human activity contributes to ocean warming and assaults on the food chain. Although the immense increase in sea lion cancers has not yet been scientifically traced to a human cause, the incidence of cancer parallels the rise in coastal populations.

The Marine Mammal Center is not interfering with nature. It is working to stop interference with nature.

Q Sea lions steal salmon from fishermen's nets and fishing lines. Don't fishermen have the right to shoot sea lions to protect their catch?

A Sea lions are excellent for good fish runs! Large salmon are fast, and sea lions rarely catch them. Small salmon are slower and more often caught by sea lions. Large fish and small fish compete to eat the same food, such as herring, pelagic amphipods, and krill. Since sea lions keep populations of small salmon in check, that means there's more food around to support the large salmon that humans enjoy. Killing a sea lion may save a fish catch in the short term but ruin the large salmon runs in the long term. The National Marine Fisheries Service conducted a study and concluded that

reduction of pinniped numbers may increase the population of other predators of commercial fish, thus reducing the population of the commercial fish because predatory fish are greater consumers of fish than marine mammals or sea birds. For example . . . because Pacific harbor seals and California sea lions are predators of lamprey, decreasing the seal and sea lion population could increase the lamprey population. Lampreys are parasites which can affect both growth and survival of salmonids; consequently, pinnipeds may benefit certain salmonid populations by limiting the lamprey population.*

Though it may be frustrating to watch sea lions kill salmon, remember that sea lions are more valuable to the salmon population alive than dead.

*Source: National Marine Fisheries Service (NMFS), "Investigation of Scientific Information on the Impacts of California Sea Lions and Pacific Harbor Seals on Salmonids and on the Coastal Ecosystems of Washington, Oregon, and California," NOAA Technical Memorandum NMFS-NWFSC-2 (1997): 172.

acknowledgments

I am deeply grateful to Ann Bauer, Jeff Boehm, Frances Gulland, Micaela Heekin, Mecca Nelson, and Jim Oswald for the time and effort they put into helping me write this book. In the true spirit of The Marine Mammal Center, this was a group effort.